Contents

Down Your Street

Models of extended community support services for people with mental health problems

Lesley Warner — *Senior Researcher, The Sainsbury Centre for Mental Health*

Richard Ford — *Head of Service Evaluation, The Sainsbury Centre for Mental Health*

Sandra Bagnall — *Researcher, The Sainsbury Centre for Mental Health*

Steve Morgan — *Training and Development Officer, The Sainsbury Centre for Mental Health*

Catriona McDaid — *Senior Research and Information Officer, Praxis Mental Health, Northern Ireland*

Sonia Mawhinney — *Research Officer, Praxis Mental Health, Northern Ireland*

ISBN: 1 870480 32 5

Published by

The Sainsbury Centre for Mental Health
134-138 Borough High Street
London
SE1 1LB

0171 403 8790

www.SainsburyCentre.org.uk

Acknowledgements

The Sainsbury Centre for Mental Health would like to thank all the organisations and individuals involved in the service evaluations on which this report is based:

▶ The staff and users of the Bexley Community Support Scheme, in particular Josie Turner and Claire Butler, senior community support workers, Amanda Doust from The National Schizophrenia Fellowship, London and South East Region, and the members of the Project Management Group.

▶ Ursula Rigert and the volunteers and users of Speke Options, the staff and users at The Leeson Centre, Speke, the staff and users of the Knowsley Community Support Project and Social Networks Project, and Robin Currie and Paula Sutton from PSS in Liverpool.

▶ The Good Neighbours and their clients from the Leathermarket Gardens Good Neighbour Scheme, Neil Collins (Project Supervisor) from the Community Support Team, Guy's and Lewisham NHS Trust, and Richard Bailey (Project Administrator) from the London Borough of Southwark Housing Department.

▶ The staff and clients of the Portadown Home Response Service, Praxis Mental Health, Northern Ireland, in particular Anne McCormack (Projects Manager), Gerald Heatley (Senior Project Worker), and staff from the Craigavon and Banbridge Community Mental Health Team.

Parts of this report are based on evaluations of a number of community-based support services, carried out by several researchers.

These are:

▶ The Bexley Community Support Scheme, evaluated by Lesley Warner (May 1997).

▶ The Leathermarket Gardens Good Neighbour Scheme, North Southwark, evaluated by Lesley Warner with additional material by Steve Morgan (May 1997).

▶ Speke Options (March 1997), the Knowsley Community Support Project and the Social Networks Project, Liverpool, (May 1997) evaluated by Sandra Bagnall.

▶ The Portadown Home Response Service, Northern Ireland, evaluated by Dr Catriona McDaid and Sonia Mawhinney, Praxis Mental Health, Northern Ireland (April 1997).

Key Points

Establishing a service:

▶ Building on existing services can have advantages, as networks with the statutory sector may already be well developed, costs may be lower, and staff absences can be covered across several small services. However, relationships with the existing services will need to be worked through. Locating a new project in the premises of an existing, high-profile mental health service might help staff to make links quickly with existing networks of other agencies. Sharing premises can also allow savings to be made on expenditure such as rent and other overheads, and in an area which is isolated and deprived, it may be easier to attract potential users to a building they already know.

▶ Although the services evaluated are deliberately local, and therefore small in scale, at least two core staff are required to develop and sustain a service.

▶ Statutory sector purchasers and the voluntary sector providers need to be realistic about the time needed to establish schemes. There may well be delays to recruitment of staff and attracting users.

▶ It is important not to underestimate the problems caused by delays in securing finance, and the vulnerability of insecure, longer-term funding, to the development and sustainability of a new service.

▶ An understanding of local politics and relationships between groups is essential in order to ensure services do not become overt rivals, destructive of each other's work, through misunderstandings and misperceived advantages. Trying to draw clients and volunteers from a small pool, from within existing services, may be seen as threatening to the more established services, and sensitive information-sharing, liaison and negotiation should precede any active recruitment of either group. It should also be remembered that other key services, in particular statutory health and social services, are likely to have had some contact with the 'host' organisation, and may view the new service in terms of whether this was positive or negative.

▶ A service which relies on offering an alternative model of care to that provided by the statutory services as its unique selling point needs to be perceived as doing this, and not associated with statutory health or social services by other local organisations.

Funding and costings:

▶ Commissioners need to understand that voluntary sector services such as those evaluated here may have high initial unit costs associated with the start-up period. Unit costs will also be higher if the service has to engage in a high level of non-direct work such as care co-ordination.

▶ Larger voluntary sector providers may be able to offer lower unit costs and to absorb the risks of more flexible funding, such as spot purchasing. However, this may in effect subsidise one service at the expense of another, which may also be funded by the same body.

► Short-term and flexible contracts will increase transaction costs and therefore unit costs, although the voluntary sector may, at least in the short term, be prepared to subsidise services through their own resources.

Management of services:

► Good management at the scheme and organisational levels will cost money and be reflected in unit costs. Like-with-like comparisons with the statutory sector are difficult to achieve and management costs may be relatively high for very small organisations. Commissioners should take a longer-term perspective and consider how sound management will help the individual service, and other new services, to develop.

► Stakeholder committees may be useful to establish new services with good inter-agency relationships. They should not necessarily have a longer-term role, and can be a difficult and cumbersome way to manage a service, but thought should be given to how local stakeholders can continue to have some input to the service.

► Purchasers may need to vary their involvement in the management of schemes over time. While there may be a need for a high level of supportive involvement at the outset, over time this may evolve into a more distinct purchaser-provider relationship and become a monitoring and reviewing role.

Aims of the service and intended clients:

► Eligibility and exclusion criteria should be carefully set so as to ensure an appropriate match between clients and support scheme staff.

► The aims of each scheme should be realistic, given the potential that users have to benefit, and the skills of the staff. In particular, thought should be given to the relative priorities accorded to existing users of the service and those waiting to use it, and how to deal either with helping some people to move on, or how to curtail new demand for the service.

► Schemes should aim to work alongside the statutory sector and complement and extend the service available. There may be some limited potential for freeing up statutory sector staff time.

Attracting referrals:

► It takes time for new services to win the confidence of professional staff and attract the right number of appropriate referrals, so implementation timetables should be realistic. Services themselves, and their funders, should be prepared for delays. Members of steering groups can often help to encourage referrals through their links with statutory services.

► Services should resist the temptation to accept inappropriate referrals in order to increase their number of clients in the early days, as this can leave them with a worse credibility problem in the long run. Dealing with inappropriate clients, and trying to disengage with them, will consume valuable resources. It is important that realistic referral criteria are established, and widely publicised, at the outset.

▶ Services should invest time in regular liaison with potential referrers, explaining the referral criteria and the service to be offered, and providing updates on progress. This should include liaison with hospital and community mental health services, social work staff and GPs, and should be an ongoing process, continuing after the service is well established.

▶ Integration between statutory mental health services and voluntary organisations can lead to a co-ordinated package of care for individuals with serious and complex needs, reducing the scope for people to 'fall through the net'.

▶ Establishing and maintaining good links between organisations needs ongoing work and commitment from both sides. Having agreed care plans alone will not ensure integrated care, but they may provide encouragement and a structure for this to happen.

Services offered:

▶ Flexibility in what is offered, and in the hours it is available, is a key element of services which are aiming to complement more traditional statutory services.

▶ Services can provide emotional, social and practical support to people within their own homes, and in the wider community, to increase their confidence and reduce social isolation.

Outcomes for users, and the views of service users, staff and key informants:

▶ In view of what the services evaluated actually provide, they cannot be said to be replacing statutory services, rather they are complementary to them, filling gaps which would not otherwise be filled. Few health trusts or social services departments would see it as their role to provide low-level social support, even to people who should clearly be among their highest priority because of their severe and enduring mental health problems. However, the provision of practical, emotional and social support by other agencies may well relieve the demand on other services for these types of activity, resulting in a more appropriate use of more highly-paid professionals' time.

▶ When evaluating support services, some objective measures can be used to assess whether users maintain or improve their social and behavioural functioning, and whether their contact with statutory services decreases. However, the subjective quality of life 'feel-good factor' is also an important indicator for services aiming to support isolated people with severe long-term mental health problems. Although there may be no objectively measured improvements in users' quality of life, if they feel better and are more positive about their lives, this is clearly a beneficial outcome.

▶ An understanding of how paid staff and volunteers feel about the various elements of their work can highlight areas in which further training or support is needed. There is likely to be tension between the satisfaction gained by seeing users improve, and possible frustration when they reach and maintain their optimum level of functioning. Working mostly on a one-to-one basis with clients can produce a trade-off between enjoying a high degree of autonomy, and feeling isolated and unsupported.

▶ It is important that local statutory services understand and respect the work of the support services, if they are to become an integrated part of the overall service provision.

Staffing issues:

▶ Devising and implementing staffing policies can be very time-consuming, but they are essential to maintaining a high standard of care. Proper support and supervision should address issues of service delivery, staff performance and development, and safety issues.

▶ It is important to match the type of staff recruited, whether professionally qualified or not, to the needs and ethos of the particular service. The number of sessional staff, and the size of their individual caseloads, also needs to be considered.

▶ There may be some difficulties in recruiting volunteers, especially in areas of high social deprivation. Publicity material, and training and preparation for the role must be geared to local needs and sensitivities. For example, services could produce a range of information leaflets, for diverse audiences, to bridge the information gap.

▶ Any project employing a small number of staff may experience difficulties in providing cover for sickness and holidays, and some voluntary organisations may have a high turnover of staff, leading to a lack of continuity for users, but these problems are not unique to the voluntary sector.

Conclusions:

▶ All the services evaluated which are still in operation were provided by voluntary organisations, and received some or all their funding from statutory sources. The voluntary sector has a reputation for being more innovative, creative and flexible than statutory services, providing an alternative model of services, which can be more responsive to the needs, and wishes of users. At the moment, voluntary organisations have a greater capacity than the statutory sector to provide flexible services, which are available 'out of hours', although statutory services are increasingly being exhorted to extend their availability in this way.

▶ Given the current climate in health and social care, it seems likely that voluntary organisations will continue to expand and develop their role as providers of services for people with mental health problems. However, as they increasingly become funded by statutory sector purchasers, and subject to rigid contract monitoring, the distinction between the sectors may be reduced or lost.

▶ These services are not replacing statutory health and social services, but are complementary to them, filling gaps which would not otherwise be filled. Providing practical, emotional and social support to people with severe and enduring mental health problems may relieve the demand on other services for these types of activity, resulting in a more appropriate use of professional staff's time.

▶ Some prejudice still exists within statutory services about working with the voluntary sector, and some may assume that using non-professionally trained staff may cause problems, that voluntary sector workers have less training than statutory workers, and that they are less accountable than statutory organisations. However, as voluntary organisations are increasingly being contracted by statutory funders to provide services to clients with serious mental health problems, the perception that they are 'amateurs' should be dispelled.

▶ In order to maximise their chances of success, voluntary organisations should not accept contracts to provide services which are beyond their remit to deliver, or which should properly be provided within the statutory sector.

► Voluntary organisations which maintain a distance from workers in statutory services, such as CPNs and social workers, run the risk of isolation. A reluctance by either sector to share necessary client-related information makes it more likely that things will go wrong.

► It is hard to compare the true costs of providing services in each sector, but there is a general perception that the voluntary sector is cheaper. When placing contracts, purchasers of these services should ensure they are looking to get good value for money, and not just buying the cheapest option, and they should devise ways of monitoring the contract which include qualitative measures of user satisfaction and the views of other key individuals and organisations, as well as quantitative data. The subjective quality of life 'feel-good factor' is also an important indicator for services aiming to support isolated people with severe long-term mental health problems, as even where there is no objectively measured improvement in users' quality of life, if they feel better and are more positive about their lives, this is clearly a beneficial outcome.

1 Introduction

The previous government's proposals for a 'Spectrum of Care' (Department of Health, 1996) to be provided for people with serious mental illness struck a chord with many health and local authority purchasers, and voluntary sector providers, who have already embarked on innovative models of delivering flexible and responsive services to people in their own homes. Domiciliary support services have become part of the package of care in many parts of England, and in Northern Ireland. This report brings together the results of the evaluations of five such services which provide support to people with severe mental illness living in their own homes. We hope that sharing this work will assist purchasers who wish to stimulate voluntary sector developments, and will be helpful to voluntary organisations who want to set up similar services.

Although the services have different forms of management, funding arrangements and staffing, they share broad aims about providing social and practical support to people with a long-term mental illness who are experiencing social isolation, and may be at risk of admission or readmission to hospital. Each service is available outside traditional 'office hours', tries to work in a flexible and imaginative way, putting the client at the centre of the activities. Aiming to match the care provider carefully with the client, they commonly offer a range of social activities. All have programmes for the recruitment, training, support and supervision of paid staff or volunteers, and have developed strategies for attracting referrals from, and working co-operatively with, local statutory health and social services. The impact of these developments for service users, based on in-depth evaluations of their satisfaction, quality of life and social functioning, is reported.

This report discusses the key issues, providing examples drawn from the evaluation work, and setting out key learning points for purchasers and providers of community support services. Information presented about the various schemes, including the numbers of clients and staff, was correct at the time the evaluations were carried out. It is likely that there will have been some changes, and the services may have developed further, since then.

2 Establishing a service

Setting up a new scheme from scratch involves a number of complex processes, and the time taken to get from the genesis of an idea to providing a service to users can vary tremendously. Practical issues, such as securing funding, finding premises and attracting staff and referrals, and philosophical considerations like agreeing the eligibility criteria and operational policy, have to be dealt with. Many of these issues are inter-dependent, and the choice of whether to recruit staff and volunteers before trying to attract referrals is a difficult one to make. On the one hand, a service does not want to have staff waiting for clients to appear, as they will quickly become demotivated and the funders will raise questions about value for money. On the other hand, it would be poor practice to raise the expectations of potential service users, only for there to be a delay while staff were recruited. Ideally, therefore, the two processes should take place simultaneously. In practice, it is rarely possible to achieve that degree of co-ordination, and projects must decide how best to resolve these issues at the local level.

Attaching a new service to an existing one, building on local goodwill, and developing connections with other services, can be a successful way of overcoming some of these difficulties. Severe delays in any stage of the process can result in a loss of momentum for the new project, which may contribute to its failure to become established and achieve the 'critical mass' needed to sustain its services.

How a support service will work within the local community, and where it will be based, should be considered at the planning stage. Proximity to the potential clients is important, as is the type of premises chosen. In many cases, pragmatic decisions have to be taken, as the best choice may be the lesser of two relatively unsuitable options, rather than something that would be ideal. Services in urban areas may have to consider different factors from those in more rural settings, where travelling times and costs may be significant. Services should consider to what extent they can integrate their clients into the wider local community, or whether they aim to provide a 'stand-alone' service.

Whether services opt for independent premises, or share those of another team or organisation, may prove significant in how the scheme is perceived by clients and referrers. Association with another service may work to the benefit or the detriment of the scheme, depending on local factors, and can ultimately effect the way the service operates and how successful it is. Establishing the separate identity of a new scheme takes time and effort, and this may be harder to achieve if it is associated with another organisation. Location of the service can be crucial even if almost all client contact takes place in peoples' homes or elsewhere.

Introducing the Portadown Home Response Service, Northern Ireland

Established in 1995, it was initially focused on the urban areas of Lurgan and Portadown, both of which have relatively high population densities. It was then extended to include the rural areas around Banbridge, covering about 30 square miles altogether.

Initially funded by a block contract with Craigavon and Banbridge Health and Social Services Trust, and The Sainsbury Centre for Mental Health, it is run by Praxis, a large voluntary organisation delivering mental health services throughout Northern Ireland.

In April 1997, the service was staffed by a part-time co-ordinator and four Home Response Workers.

Available between 9 am and 9 pm, 7 days a week, offering companionship, emotional support, practical support, monitoring of mental health and active intervention, participation in social and leisure activities outside the home. Also liaises with statutory services, families and carers.

Providing 100 care hours a week in 1997, the scheme supported 49 clients during the year.

Further information is available from:
Praxis Home Response Service, 15 Hanover Street, Portadown, County Armagh, Northern Ireland BT62 3LN.

▶ The Portadown Home Response Service (HRS) in Northern Ireland provides an example of how a new service can be attached to an existing one, successfully building on established networks, and utilising shared office accommodation and a larger staff pool.

▶ Praxis had been operating two accommodation and support schemes within the Craigavon and Banbridge Health and Social Services Trust area for some years. There were good existing communication links and liaison both at senior management level and with field level staff, so the lengthy process of a new organisation establishing its credentials with local statutory agencies was avoided. This existing relationship provided a foundation for agreeing the service specification with the Trust, disseminating information about the service to the local community mental health team (CMHT), and making the service operational, so that referrals commenced soon after the service started.

▶ There were also a number of operational advantages to attaching the HRS to an existing accommodation scheme, including cost benefits to having existing management structures in place, and being able to share office accommodation. The HRS co-ordinator worked part-time both for the HRS and in the accommodation scheme, allowing some flexibility in relation to their availability for staff, and facilitated liaison with the CMHT. Additionally, there were two other professionally graded staff in the accommodation scheme who could provide cover in the absence of the HRS co-ordinator, and others from the accommodation service could cover for absent HRS workers. Providing cover for leave and sickness absence in small 'standalone' services, which do not have this built-in access to back-up, can be difficult.

Introducing the Leathermarket Gardens Good Neighbour Scheme, North Southwark

Established in 1995, and in operation until March 1997, the scheme was located on an inner city, multi-cultural local authority housing estate with a population of 13,200, in the London Borough of Southwark. A Jarman UPA score of 49.95 for the borough indicates severe deprivation.

Jointly funded by the London Borough of Southwark and Lambeth, Southwark & Lewisham Health Authority, it was run by two staff from Lewisham and Guy's Mental Health Trust's community support team who acted as part-time project manager and project supervisor, and a housing officer from the local authority housing department who acted as a part-time project administrator. Unpaid volunteers were recruited from the same estate to be Good Neighbours.

With flexible hours of availability, including evenings and weekends, it offered day-to-day social contact, emotional support, and a point of access to statutory services.

Originally intended to provide support to between 25 and 35 clients, in March 1997 the scheme had 5 clients and 5 good neighbours. It is no longer taking new referrals.

Further information is available from:
Steve Morgan, Training and Development Officer, The Sainsbury Centre for Mental Health, 134-138 Borough High Street, London SE1 1LB.

▶ Located within the statutory sector, the Leathermarket Gardens Good Neighbour Scheme in North Southwark suffered from severe delays in securing and receiving funding, which contributed to its ultimate failure to achieve sustainability.

▶ The London Borough of Southwark had identified befriending schemes as a priority for service development, particularly for the mental health client group. Lewisham & Guy's Mental Health NHS Trust submitted a project proposal, on the basis of the knowledge of mental health issues developed through the experience of the local community support team. In this way an agency partnership was developed between Southwark Housing Department and the Trust.

▶ The Leathermarket Gardens Neighbourhood area was targeted for a pilot project on the basis of its strongly established links between the statutory housing department and tenants' associations managed by a Joint Management Board. The foundation was in place to forge a partnership between local tenants, Southwark Housing and the Health Trust.

▶ At the point when joint finance was agreed, the project had already suffered a number of setbacks and delays in securing funding, the process having originally started in 1994-95. Although funding had been agreed from a Southwark social services Transitional Special Grant in 1994, this was eventually lost, and an arrangement for the Care Management budget to make up the shortfall in funding between January and April 1995, when the joint finance was to start, was not confirmed until February of that year. These delays all had an impact on the momentum of the project, and the final year's funding for 1997-1998 was not sought, although the service continued to support its existing clients.

15

Introducing the Bexley Community Support Scheme

The scheme was established in late 1995 in the London Borough of Bexley, which has a population of 215,615 and a Jarman score of -11.64, indicating a low level of deprivation.

It was funded jointly by the London Borough of Bexley and Bexley & Greenwich Health Authority, and managed by the National Schizophrenia Fellowship London and South East Region (NSF LASER).

In December 1996, it employed two full-time and two part-time salaried staff, and 14 sessional staff.

Available between 9 am and 9 pm, seven days a week, the scheme offers emotional support, help with practical and household tasks, and assistance with social and independent living skills.

Intended to support about 40 people, it had 34 clients at the end of 1996.

Further information is available from:
The Bexley Community Support Service, c/o The Crayford Centre, 4-6 London Road, Crayford, Kent DA1 4BH.

▶ The Bexley Community Support Scheme (BSS) experienced delays in becoming operational, mainly due to difficulty recruiting senior staff, which created tensions for purchasers, and the multi-agency group responsible for establishing it.

▶ Joint local authority and health funding was agreed for the service in the 1994/95 financial year, with funding due to start in April 1995, by which time a Project Manager was expected to be in post. However, two recruitment drives nationally and within the National Schizophrenia Fellowship (NSF) were unsuccessful. Eventually, two staff were recruited to more junior-graded posts, and the project began in October 1995, an adjustment being made to the timing of the financial arrangements to ensure the service did not lose six months funding for the period when it had been unable to start.

▶ Differences of opinion among the multi-agency group which brought together the culture, practices and policies of many organisations, about the type of person they were looking for, was one of the factors thought to have affected staff recruitment. Some of the statutory sector representatives wanted to appoint an experienced professional, either a social worker or a mental health nurse, while some from the voluntary sector wanted a manager with a non-institutional background in a voluntary organisation. There were also tensions between the agencies funding the project and those managing it, about the recruitment process.

▶ The different salary expectations between statutory and voluntary agencies may also have contributed to the initial recruitment problems, and the post was regraded to a higher level. Workers coming from the statutory sector were thought to expect a higher salary than is the norm in voluntary organisations, and this posed problems for the NSF as the grading had to be compatible with their overall salary structure to prevent any anomalies between this post and that of their line manager.

Introducing Speke Options, Liverpool

Established in late 1994, the project is located in Speke, an isolated area on the outskirts of Liverpool with a population of approximately 11,000, and a Jarman UPA score of 37.92, indicating a high level of deprivation.

It was initially funded for two years by The Sainsbury Centre for Mental Health, and it is run by PSS, a large voluntary organisation that provides a range of services to people in north west England.

In March 1997, the scheme had one paid worker – a 0.8 whole time equivalent (wte) Development Worker, and 5 volunteers. Support for the paid worker was provided by the Project Manager.

Available at flexible times, including evenings and weekends, it provides personal support, activities and training to individuals and groups of clients.

Initially intended to support 25 to 30 people, in March 1997 it had 21 clients.

Further information is available from:
Speke Options, c/o The Leeson Centre, 115-117 Alderwood Road, Speke, Liverpool L15 7RB.

▶ The task of establishing a service can be even more daunting and time-consuming when it is left to just one part-time worker, who is responsible for both recruiting volunteers and attracting referrals. Speke Options provides an example of a service operating with only one paid worker, but which also aimed to utilise local goodwill through being part of an established voluntary organisation and located within an existing user-led drop-in centre which is the only mental health resource in the area.

▶ Before the Development Worker was appointed in September 1994, a steering group had been established which was involved in extensive networking with outside agencies. PSS's role as a local provider of services was helpful in providing credibility for the new service, and the worker's initial tasks were to network with all agencies based in Speke, to develop relationships with potential service users, and to establish the identity of the service within the drop-in centre.

▶ The first users were engaged at the end of 1994, and the first volunteer was recruited in March 1995. Unfortunately, the first volunteers were interested in facilitating specific activities, and there were no 'general' volunteers to act as a buffer between the worker and the service users. This meant that the worker could not engage all of the new referrals, and a short-term waiting list was created, putting added pressure on the worker, the referrers and the potential clients.

▶ One means of maximising the limited available resources was to offer many activities to groups of users, rather than individuals, although some users continued to receive individual support in addition to, or instead of, group activities.

Introducing The Knowsley Community Support Service (CSS) and the Social Networks Project (SNP)

The CSS, established in 1994, is based in Huyton, the part of Knowsley with the highest number of people with severe mental health problems. The SNP is based in Kirkby, which has the second highest number of people with severe mental health problems.

The schemes are funded by spot purchasing by local authority social services Care Managers as part of a package of community care, with some additional core funding from St Helens and Knowsley Health Authority. They are run by PSS, a large voluntary organisation, which provides a range of services to people in the north west of England.

In May 1997, the CSS had a manager and nineteen support workers, 17 of whom were sessional workers. The SNP had a full time manager and two part time support workers.

The availability of both CSS and SNP are flexible, with hours being negotiable with users, including evenings and weekends. A wide range of supportive, practical and social activities is offered, inside and outside the home, some events being run on a group basis.

In May 1997 the Community Support Service had 17 clients. The Social Networks Project had around 60 clients, about half of whom were engaged in activities on a weekly basis.

Further information is available from:
Project Manager, Social Networking, PSS, 18 Seel Street, Liverpool L1 4BE.

▶ The Community Support Service (CSS) developed from an existing reprovision service providing accommodation for former long-stay hospital inpatients, and the Social Networks Project (SNP) developed from an outreach project. There were advantages for both new services in being part of PSS's wide network of provision across the area.

Learning Points:

▶ Building on existing services can have advantages, as networks with the statutory sector may already be well developed, costs may be lower, and staff absences can be covered across several small services. However, relationships with the existing services will need to be worked through. Locating a new project in the premises of an existing, high-profile mental health service might help staff to make links quickly with existing networks of other agencies. Sharing premises can also allow savings to be made on expenditure such as rent and other overheads, and in an area which is isolated and deprived, it may be easier to attract potential users to a building they already know.

▶ Although these services are deliberately local, and therefore small in scale, at least two core staff are required to develop and sustain a service.

▶ Purchasers and the voluntary sector providers need to be realistic about the time needed to establish schemes. There may well be delays to recruitment of staff and attracting users.

▶ It is important not to underestimate the problems caused by delays in securing finance, and the vulnerability of longer-term funding, to the development and sustainability of a new service.

▶ An understanding of local politics and relationships between groups is essential in order to ensure services do not become overt rivals, destructive of each other's work, through misunderstandings and misperceived advantages. Trying to draw clients and volunteers from a small pool, from within existing services, may be seen as threatening to the more established services, and sensitive information-sharing, liaison and negotiation should precede any active recruitment of either group. It should also be remembered that other key services, in particular statutory health and social services, are likely to have had some contact with the 'host' organisation, and may view the new service in terms of whether this was positive or negative.

▶ A service which relies on offering an alternative model of care to that provided by the statutory services as its unique selling point needs to be perceived as doing this, and not associated with statutory health or social services by other local organisations.

3 Funding and costings

Local authority social services departments and health authorities fund most of the health and social care provided by both the statutory and voluntary sectors. The services examined in this report were all funded by the statutory authorities, and as the diversity of services develops along the continuum of care, it is likely that this will continue.

Funders will always be concerned to ensure they get value for their money, but no current data provides exact guidelines for comparing costs between services run within the voluntary sector, and statutory mental health and social services. Like with like comparisons, therefore, are very hard to make, and this chapter provides a starting point, rather than the last word, on costings.

The best source of comparative data relating to statutory services has been used to provide a rough benchmark for calculating costs per hour of care of the services described. The figures available for 1995/96 were used for comparison with data collected during this period (Netten & Dennett, 1996). The following table shows a range of costs per care hour, to which those of other services may be compared, depending on what is being provided.

Table 1

Staff group	Cost per care hour
Community mental health worker	£62
Community psychiatric nurse	£47
Auxiliary nurse	£21
Social worker (generic caseload)	£12
Local authority home care worker	£8

The Bexley Community Support Scheme

► The Bexley Community Support Service was funded jointly by the local authority and health authority, with a 'funding agreement' being devised to set out the level of service provided. The total revenue costs of the service in 1996/97 were £128,271, not including the costs of renting premises, which were provided free of charge by Social Services. Activity data for the service showed a total of 3,274.4 hours of direct client care were provided by all staff (including core staff and sessional support workers) in a six month period between September 1996 and February 1997. Making an estimate of £1,900 per annum for capital overheads, based on data from the PSSRU, the unit cost was calculated as £19.86 per care hour. In terms of cost per care hour provided, BSS was not cheap to provide. However, it was a high quality service representing good value for money, as although the sessional support workers could be compared to unqualified community mental health team staff, the senior BSS staff, with their added responsibility for the assessment, planning and monitoring of care, supervision of staff, and liaison with other organisations, were more comparable to qualified CMHT members.

▶ Whether joint funding would continue beyond the agreed period was becoming a concern to the project, as there were suggestions that cuts by statutory purchasers might affect them. Not knowing if the service would continue, or be able to develop further, was felt to be unsettling for, and possibly detrimental to, their clients.

Portadown Home Response Service

▶ Portadown Home Response Service was initially funded by Craigavon and Banbridge Health and Social Services Trust (CBHSST) and The Sainsbury Centre for Mental Health, and had total revenue costs in 1996/97 of £37,400. A service agreement/service protocol between Praxis and CBHSST set out the aims and objectives of the service, criteria for referral, the process for referral and review, and monitoring and quality assurance. Providing 100 hours per week in April 1997 with between 90 and 95 hours spent on direct care, the unit cost is £7.20 per hour, which represents good value for money, given the range of support provided.

Speke Options and other PSS services

▶ Speke Options was initially funded for two years by The Sainsbury Centre for Mental Health, who also funded the evaluation of the service. The total revenue costs for 1995/ 96 were £28,258. The unit cost is £10.60 per hour, representing good value for money, as the role of the paid worker was to create more care through the use of volunteers.

▶ There were some concerns about securing continued funding for Speke Options once the initial funding period ended, and about having raised users' expectations by providing a service which might close. Although possible funding sources were identified at an early stage, there were long delays in the process of negotiation which resulted in uncertainty.

▶ This uncertainty about continued funding was of concern to professionals, as it was thought this might lead them to regard Speke Options as a short-term service, making them reluctant to refer new clients to it and having a negative impact on the service's development.

▶ PSS's Community Support Services were purchased through spot contracts by Care Managers, for example local authority social workers or community psychiatric nurses (CPNs), as part of a package of community care services. The service also received some core funding from St Helens and Knowsley Health Authority, which reduced the rate from £8.70 to £7.50 per care hour, representing good value for money.

▶ The PSS Social Networks Project had a unit cost of £2.56 per care hour, representing very good value for money, and reflecting the small number of staff and the large number of clients engaged with the service.

The Leathermarket Gardens Good Neighbour Scheme

▶ The Leathermarket Gardens Good Neighbour Scheme in North Southwark received joint finance from the local authority and health authority of £25,000 a year, for three years, of which £1,000 each year was for the evaluation of the service. However, there was an underspend of £2,700 in 1995-96, and of £6,000 in 1996/97, which was clawed back by joint finance. The third year's funding (1997/98) was not applied for. It is not possible to calculate the unit cost per care hour from the data provided, although with the small number of clients the scheme attracted this is likely to be high in comparison with the other services.

Learning Points:

- ▶ Commissioners need to understand that voluntary sector services such as those evaluated here may have high initial unit costs associated with the start-up period. Unit costs will also be higher if the service has to engage in a high level of non-direct work such as care co-ordination.

- ▶ Larger voluntary sector providers may be able to offer lower unit costs and to absorb the risks of more flexible funding, such as spot purchasing. However, this may in effect subsidise one service at the expense of another, which may also be funded by the same body.

- ▶ Short-term and flexible contracts will increase transaction costs and therefore unit costs, although the voluntary sector may, at least in the short term, be prepared to subsidise services through their own resources.

4 Management of services

There are complex issues to be resolved when considering how the work of a project should best be managed. For example, there may be tensions between the roles of steering groups and managers of services, with the former wanting to take some responsibility for guiding the service's work. These were particular issues for two of the services evaluated.

The Bexley Community Support Scheme

▶ The establishment of the Bexley Support Scheme (BSS) was managed by a multi-agency group of representatives from local health and social services purchasers and providers, and a number of voluntary organisations. Individuals from a range of backgrounds and ideologies worked well to draw up a flexible operational policy, decide on the criteria and process for referrals, and recruit staff. However, the group's ongoing role was less successful, with members being much less clear about its abilities and responsibilities. Confusion about its role led to the group ceasing to meet after the service had been running for about a year, which resulted in a number of local organisations losing their opportunity to discuss and make comments on the ongoing work and development of the service. While it may be appropriate for project management to be undertaken by one individual, it would also be useful to have a forum in which other interested parties could contribute their views.

▶ There were advantages and disadvantages to the BSS of being established by a large, national voluntary organisation. It clearly benefited from being part of an organisation which had experience of setting up new schemes, and was used to developing operational policies and dealing with recruitment, personnel, and equal opportunities issues. However, some key informants in other local services questioned whether the management fee charged by the 'parent' organisation for these tasks was reasonable, and others felt the organisation's national structure, with the project's line manager based a long way away, made it less able to be in tune with, and responsive to, local needs and wishes.

▶ The BSS came under pressure from the health and local authority funders to start delivering a service while they were still trying to recruit project staff. Statutory sector purchasers increasingly expect voluntary sector organisations that apply to them for funding to show financial sophistication and the ability to adhere to a strict implementation timetable. In their turn, the purchasers may lack a detailed understanding of the realities of setting up a service from scratch, and their funding cycle may make it hard for them to respond flexibly to changing circumstances. Staff in both sectors would benefit from a greater understanding of each other's pressures and constraints.

Speke Options

▶ Speke Options, run by PSS, had a steering group in place before the Development Worker was recruited. This Group played an extremely valuable role, undertaking extensive networking within their own statutory and voluntary organisations, and ensuring that colleagues knew about and made referrals to the service. They also had a key role in defining the service and the criteria for accepting referrals, helping to design the publicity material and referral forms, with regular input from the Sainsbury Centre for Mental Health. The members worked well together, were positive and supportive of each other, and were committed to the project's success. This consistent involvement ensured they all had a stake in the service, and a sense of ownership evolved.

▶ Although potential sources of future funding were identified early on, the group had little experience of the procedure and timescales of statutory funding cycles, and the process of negotiation proved to be lengthy, problematic and stressful. This meant that the group spent a lot of time on funding issues, and the planning and development of the service were given a lower priority. The 'parent' voluntary organisation also needed to be more involved in the process of bidding, as they had a great deal of experience in negotiating a range of contracts with statutory funding agencies.

Learning Points:

▶ Good management at the scheme and organisational levels will cost money and be reflected in unit costs. Like-with-like comparisons with the statutory sector are difficult to achieve and management costs may be relatively high for very small organisations. Commissioners should take a longer term perspective and consider how sound management will help the individual service, and other new services, to develop.

▶ Stakeholder committees may be useful to establish new services with good inter-agency relationships. They should not necessarily have a longer term role, and can be a difficult and cumbersome way to manage a service, but thought should be given to how local stakeholders can continue to have some input to the service.

▶ Purchasers may need to vary their involvement in the management of schemes over time. While there may be a need for a high level of supportive involvement at the outset, over time this may evolve into a more distinct purchaser-provider relationship and become a monitoring and reviewing role.

5 Aims of the service and intended clients

The aims of all the services evaluated had many similarities in terms of the client groups they were trying to reach and the type of activities offered.

The Intended Client Groups

Establishing criteria for referrals to extended community support services is essential to ensure the service reaches the client group for which it was intended and, indeed, funded. Purchasers are rightly wary of services which start by focusing on those most in need but drift over time towards clients with less severe mental health problems. All the services examined here have criteria which enable them to target their resources at people with long-term and enduring problems who are also socially isolated.

A definition of eligibility criteria from Speke Options

Clients must be local residents, aged over 18, and with severe mental health needs, the definition of which encompasses a combination of diagnosis, disability and duration of their difficulties. Their diagnosis is likely to be one of schizophrenia, severe affective disorder, or other serious conditions, and this is likely to cause sufficient disability to seriously impair their functioning in any aspect of daily living. They are likely to have had the disorder for at least six months, and to feel isolated and insecure, and be on the edge of existing support services.

Portadown Home Response Service policy for people they cannot work with

Clients must not be in an acute phase of mental illness, nor suffering from a mental or physical disability, or drug or alcohol abuse, which prevents them from coping with the emotional, practical and social demands of living at home. Referrals must not have an ongoing problem of violence or any other difficulty which makes them a danger to themselves or their community, and both they and, where applicable, their family members, should understand the nature of the scheme and agree to be considered for the service offered.

Some services, such as Speke Options, were able to take referrals from any source, including self-referrals. Others, including the Bexley Community Support Scheme, accepted referrals only from a statutory sector keyworker, usually a CPN or social worker, of individuals subject to the care programme approach and local authority care management. In general, the schemes with qualified staff accepted clients with a higher level of need than those with regular staff without a formal qualification, followed by schemes employing a high proportion of sessional staff, while the volunteer schemes worked with the lowest levels of need. In addition to eligibility criteria, these voluntary sector schemes also excluded people with certain difficult or dangerous behaviour. The difficulties of engaging with isolated individuals, who might be fearful or suspicious of the service offered, should not be underestimated.

The Intended Service

While each scheme had its own individually tailored aims, there were many similarities in how they intended to help their clients. In general the aim was to provide practical, emotional and social support, reducing individuals' isolation, promoting independence and improving quality of life, and with a high degree of integration with the community. This was seen as something that statutory services would find more difficult, and thus the new schemes aimed to be complementary to existing services. On occasion, aims were included because they enhanced the potential for funding from purchasers. In particular, several schemes said they aimed to reduce the use of hospital in-patient care, despite there being no research evidence that voluntary sector schemes of this nature had ever achieved this objective. The activities provided by each scheme are set out in detail in Chapter 7.

Moving On

To what extent a service should indefinitely support its existing clients, and the issue of whether, how and when clients should move on from it, both in recognition of their increased independence and also to allow new referrals to be taken on, has not been effectively resolved. If services are to be provided in the long term, to people who, after all, have long-term difficulties, and may have experienced the process of engagement, support and rejection from a number of other agencies, it effectively means that services are closed to new referrals as soon as they are working to full capacity. It needs to be debated with the services' funders to what extent they expect to see a throughput of clients, or whether they are satisfied to purchase a service for a finite group of users.

The Bexley Community Support Scheme

▶ By the middle of 1997, BSS was working to capacity, with new referrals placed on a waiting list before they could be taken on. Although the service aimed to provide ongoing support, assuming long-term contact to be beneficial, it may be necessary to discharge some clients to make way for others who need it. Further work will need to be done by the project staff, in collaboration with the managers and funders of the service, to agree how the service should evolve, and the priority that should be afforded to existing and potential service users.

Portadown Home Response Service

▶ Many of the individuals using the Home Response Service were very isolated and, apart from contact with the CMHT, were reluctant to use other services. This could leave them particularly vulnerable to becoming dependent on the Home Response Worker. No specific concerns were raised about how the Home Response service had been operating to date, but the risk for creation of dependencies was raised as a potential area for concern with this particular service model.

Learning points:

▶ Eligibility and exclusion criteria should be carefully set so as to ensure an appropriate match between clients and support scheme staff.

▶ The aims of each scheme should be realistic, given the potential that users have to benefit, and the skills of the staff. In particular, thought should be given to the relative priorities accorded to existing users of the service and those waiting to use it, and how to deal either with helping some people to move on, or how to curtail new demand for the service.

▶ Schemes should aim to work alongside the statutory sector and complement and extend the service available. There may be some limited potential for freeing up statutory sector staff time.

6 **Attracting referrals**

A newly established project has to gain the trust of potential referral agencies, and attract clients. This is another 'chicken and egg' situation. How can the service prove to the referrers that it can be trusted to work with their clients, while the professionals are waiting to see evidence of the service's quality before making referrals? Caution on the part of referrers, although understandable, will contribute to the delays in a service becoming operational.

Staff in new services may be anxious to show what they can do, frustrated by a lack of referrals and under pressure from the purchasers to demonstrate some client-based activity, so may be tempted to accept almost any referral in the early days. These may turn out to include some individuals who, if they were referred after the service was well established, would not meet the referral criteria. Inappropriate referrals may also be accepted if referrers fail to provide all the necessary information on which to base a decision on eligibility. Working with the 'wrong' clients will not help a service establish its credibility with the referring agencies, and will divert energy away from the real target group. These referrals should be resisted, and time spent instead on building up a trusting relationship with the other agencies and providing clear information about the referral criteria.

People using community support services, which are aimed at people with serious mental illness, are extremely likely also to be in contact with the statutory health and social services. Indeed, for some support schemes, having a statutory key worker is a requirement for acceptance. Therefore, liaison between all agencies involved is crucial, to ensure services share relevant information and work together towards agreed client-centred goals. Engaging with statutory services involves far more than simply informing them of the existence of the new project; ongoing and persistent contact needs to continue, even in the face of initial suspicion, indifference or hostility. Support services can in effect model good practice, by keeping the statutory services informed, in the hope that this will eventually be reciprocated.

Many statutory services, operating within the framework of the Care Programme Approach and Care Management, are striving to integrate these two administrative systems. Whether one or two systems are in operation, statutory sector key workers should be involving staff from the voluntary projects in care planning and reviews, inviting them to attend meetings and supplying written summary reports, so that all aspects of the users' lives and activities can be considered.

The Bexley Community Support Scheme

► When the Bexley Support Scheme was first established, a locally-agreed system for integrating the Care Programme Approach and a Community Care package was starting to be implemented by the health trust and the local authority social services department, as the Bexley Care Package (BCP). Clients eligible for the BSS were expected to be on the top two tiers of the CPA and needing a high level of the BCP. As the system was new to all concerned, and the process was not at first applied uniformly across agencies, some clients' BCP levels were incorrectly given, or no BCP level was recorded at all, so that some inappropriate referrals were accepted. Some professionals were initially reluctant to share all the appropriate information with BSS, so some clients were accepted who might not have been if the full facts had been known.

Leathermarket Gardens Good Neighbour Scheme

▶ When establishing the Leathermarket Gardens Good Neighbour Scheme, publicising the service to other local agencies outside the Community Support Team resulted in support being expressed for the idea, but no client referrals were forthcoming from the main local GP practices or the Social Services mental health team. In retrospect, it was felt that assumptions should not be made, either about the willingness of potential clients to engage with a local community that they may perceive to be hostile or threatening towards them, or about the established local services welcoming the chance to make referrals to the new project.

Speke Options

▶ Speke Options experienced particular difficulties in attracting referrals. This was partly due to there being just one part-time worker who was simultaneously responsible for recruiting, training, supporting and supervising volunteers. Also, as the original eligibility criteria had been revised and tightened by the time the service started, many of those originally envisaged as potential users were no longer appropriate, while some individuals had died and others had moved out of the area. In the early stages of the project, many professionals did not know what was being provided, so were unable to explain it to their clients, the potential users, which contributed to the lack of referrals.

Learning points:

▶ It takes time for new services to win the confidence of professional staff and attract the right number of appropriate referrals, so implementation timetables should be realistic. Services themselves, and their funders, should be prepared for delays. Members of steering groups can often help to encourage referrals through their links with statutory services.

▶ Services should resist the temptation to accept inappropriate referrals in order to increase their number of clients in the early days, as this can leave them with a worse credibility problem in the long run. Dealing with inappropriate clients, and trying to disengage with them, will consume valuable resources. It is important that realistic referral criteria are established and widely publicised at the outset.

▶ Services should invest time in regular liaison with potential referrers, explaining the referral criteria and the service to be offered, and providing updates on progress. This should include liaison with hospital and community mental health services, social work staff and GPs, and should be an ongoing process, continuing after the service is well established.

▶ Integration between statutory mental health services and voluntary organisations can lead to a co-ordinated package of care for individuals with serious and complex needs, reducing the scope for people to 'fall through the net'.

▶ Establishing and maintaining good links between organisations needs ongoing work and commitment from both sides. Having agreed care plans alone will not ensure integrated care, but they may provide encouragement and a structure for this to happen.

7 Services offered

All the services evaluated provided emotional, practical and social support for their clients, both within the individual's home and outside in the wider community. Each service aimed to be user-led in terms of what was offered, tailoring the service to meet individual needs, and all were available outside the traditional office hours of 9 to 5, Monday to Friday. Some services saw clients mostly on a one-to-one basis, with occasional group activities, while others worked specifically with groups of users. In all cases the emphasis was on doing things *with* people, rather than *for* them.

The services offered mostly to individuals were:

within the home	emotional support	companionship, someone to talk to, watch TV with
		motivation and planning, setting goals
	practical support	household tasks, e.g. cooking, cleaning, decorating
		writing letters, claiming benefits
outside the home	social support	having a meal in a cafe or a drink in a pub, going to Bingo
		going for a walk in a park or gardens
		going to church
		accessing local social networks
	practical support	collecting children from school
		using public transport
		shopping
		keeping appointments, e.g. with GP, outpatients, DSS
	leisure activities	taking part in sports, e.g. swimming, aerobics, bowling
		watching sports, e.g. Speedway
liaison		liaison with statutory agencies
		liaison with families and carers

In addition, the services offered mostly to groups included social get-togethers in the evenings, either for all users or for particular groups, such as women only. Other groups met for art, or sporting activities such as using a gym, going swimming or bowling, playing badminton, or sailing. Some services organised spontaneously or 'one-off' activities, such as going to the cinema, playing snooker, or attending a sporting fixture, while others included day trips, weekend outings and residential 'mini-breaks'. One service ran a catering group where users could learn and practise cooking skills.

Bexley Community Support Scheme

▶ Support workers from the BSS helped a client to cope after coming out of hospital, both with the practical issues and tackling the problem of low self-esteem and diminished confidence. In another instance, workers helped to support and motivate a client who wanted to make the transition from a hostel to a flat of their own. One client was helped to manage their own finances and pay bills on time, while a worker encouraged another to draw up lists of things which needed to be done, such as decorating, in their new flat. Going out for specific activities like swimming, bowling, playing Bingo, aerobics and watching Speedway, were popular with many clients, while others concentrated on travelling on buses or trains, going shopping, walking in parks and gardens, or going for a meal or a drink. Sometimes several support workers took a number of their clients on joint outings, which helped to extend their social networks, and it was felt appropriate for some clients to have more than one co-worker.

Portadown Home Response Scheme

▶ The Portadown Home Response Workers' role included establishing a routine with a service user of going for brief trips to the local shops for essentials, gradually building up to longer trips to further destinations, going out for walks, or to church, or to collect prescriptions or pay bills. Clients were accompanied to leisure facilities, and information was provided on healthy eating, and assistance given with cooking. Companionship, emotional support, encouraging social and leisure activities, and social interaction activities outside the home were the most commonly requested activities. Liaison with statutory services, and links with families and carers, was also an important component of the work. Although, generally available between 9 am and 9 pm, seven days a week, the service was not used much after 5 pm or at weekends, possibly because some of the statutory keyworkers were not aware of its availability outside normal working hours.

Leathermarket Gardens Good Neighbour Scheme

▶ The Good Neighbours in the Leathermarket Gardens Scheme provided a source of day-to-day social contact, although they were not seen as a replacement for social services provision. They provided emotional support to their clients but were not expected to provide confidential counselling or health advice. Good neighbours were a point of access to, but not an alternative to, any statutory services needed by the client. While most good neighbours provided a contact at home in the local area, and an introduction to other local social networks, one also successfully acted as an advocate on a client's behalf where statutory workers had failed, and arranged for the client's flat to be redecorated by the housing department.

Speke Options

▶ Speke Options provided personal support, activities and training to individuals and groups of clients. The groups were facilitated by volunteers, with support from the development worker, allowing service users to develop companionship and build confidence in a non-stigmatising way, after which some people went on to arrange their own social events independently. A catering group, facilitated by a volunteer who was a trained chef, provided users with practical skills. It also had a social aspect, with users deciding what to cook and then sharing the meal, helping to build confidence, and enabling them to care for themselves.

PSS Social Networks Project

► PSS's Social Networks Project matched people according to their interests, and a range of activities were offered. Some activities were run on a weekly basis while others happened spontaneously in response to users' wishes. As far as possible, activities took place in local facilities like the sports centre, bingo hall, village hall, pubs and clubs.

Learning points:

► Flexibility in what is offered, and in the hours it is available, is a key element of services which are aiming to complement more traditional statutory services.

► Services can provide emotional, social and practical support to people within their own homes, and in the wider community, to increase their confidence and reduce social isolation.

8 Outcomes for users, and the views of service users, staff and key informants

Each of the evaluations set out to establish: who uses the service; do they maintain or improve their social functioning; does the package of statutory care delivered change; how is the community support service provided; how do service users, community carers and other interested parties view the scheme? Information was sought on the cost of providing each service, so that unit costs could be calculated and compared with published benchmarks.

For most of the services, socio-demographic information was collected on service users, along with details of their mental health history and the current package of care being delivered. Keyworkers were asked to complete a standardised questionnaire designed to measure social and behavioural functioning, the Life Skills Profile, both at the time of referral and at a later stage, in order to measure any change (Rosen et al.; 1989). For some services, researchers also collected information on users' inpatient bed use for a period before and after engaging with the support service.

Interviews were carried out with a number of service users, compromising a semi-structured interview and a standardised rating scale measuring satisfaction with services (Larsen et al.; 1979), and a quality of life interview schedule (Lehman, 1983), adapted by Ford (1998, unpublished PhD thesis).

Other key individuals, including support workers, service managers, staff in statutory health and social services and purchasers, were also interviewed, many of whom praised the voluntary sector's informality, flexibility, and user-centred approach, and thought that users often preferred to receive services from non-statutory organisations which they saw as independent, less stigmatising, and having more empathy with the clients. Voluntary organisations were also described as having the freedom to be more innovative than statutory services, and their track record of user involvement was valued.

Some key findings and conclusions from the evaluations are summarised below.

The Bexley Community Support Scheme

▶ In the first year of operation, the scheme received 84 referrals, of which 56 were accepted. At the end of December 1996 it was supporting 34 clients.

▶ A sample of clients who had been in contact with the scheme for at least six months expressed high levels of satisfaction with the service they received, as described in semi-structured qualitative interviews, and assessed using the Larsen questionnaire.

▶ Clients who had used the scheme for six months showed a modest improvement in their level of social functioning, and a more marked reduction in their use of inpatient psychiatric services in the six months after engagement, both of which were statistically significant.

► Interviews with ten people who had been using the service for six months or more elicited a wide range of activities. As well as enjoying the activities, most people said they also valued their conversations with the support worker while taking part. Two people had enjoyed outings with other clients and their support workers.

► Interviews were conducted with the eight support workers whose clients had been interviewed. Asked what aspects of their role they enjoyed the most, half liked seeing people improve, and others mentioned getting satisfaction from working in a client-centred and empowering way. Some liked the autonomy, responsibility and challenge of the role, and others mentioned the sheer variety, and the enjoyment they got from the activities they undertook with their clients. The least liked aspects of the role were to do with seeing clients becoming ill or even committing suicide. Most workers had contact with their clients' professional workers, and were regularly invited to review meetings. They were generally very enthusiastic about the effect BSS had on their clients, while retaining realistic expectations about their likely progress, and acknowledging that many people would need long-term support from the scheme.

► The senior staff and support workers were committed to their work, and derived satisfaction from it. Personnel issues within the service had been well thought out, with satisfactory arrangements in place for regular supervision, and access to outside counsellors if necessary.

► The service was well integrated with local mental health and social services, and effective communication between BSS and the statutory services was established through the determined and ongoing efforts of the BSS staff. However, BSS was less well integrated with other local voluntary sector organisations, to the extent that many agencies did not think it was a voluntary sector project.

Portadown Home Response Service

► Fifteen users participated in the evaluation. Using a standardised rating scale to measure social and behavioural functioning (the Life Skills Profile), there were significant improvements in the sub-scales dealing with social contact, communication and responsibility. These changes occurred between the point of referral to the service and six months after starting to receive it, with no further changes during the subsequent six months.

► On the whole, clients were very positive about the service. In each of the areas covered by the Larsen Questionnaire, all the clients interviewed gave the service the highest or second rating. In particular, almost all said they would 'definitely' recommend the service to a friend who was in need of similar help, and three-quarters rated the service as 'excellent'.

► There was limited use of the service as a short-term support system, with a tendency to use the service for long time periods, most people having used the service for at least a year before discontinuing.

► Just over half of service users were living with others, primarily in some kind of family setting. Additionally, almost a quarter had parental responsibilities. Therefore, while the service was very much focused on the individual with mental health problems referred to the service, much of the work was carried out in the context of a family setting.

► Most commonly, service users were receiving two hours Home Response time per week. Short visits were sometimes felt to be rushed for both service user and the keyworker, and too short for getting the individual "out and about". Given that encouraging social interaction outside the home and accompanying people on social outings was one of the primary reasons for referral to the service, the length of visits should be looked at in relation to this issue.

▶ Interviews with a number of home response Workers (HRWs) identified some areas of particular satisfaction in their work, and some concerns. They found the training sessions on aggressive and violent behaviour, and on accountability, to be very useful, and there was a high level of satisfaction with the ongoing supervision and support received. Short visits with service users were sometimes experienced as rushed, although long sessions could sometimes be experienced as very tiring and draining. HRWs attended review meetings with professional workers and felt that their contribution was taken into consideration.

▶ Asked what particular aspects of their job that they particularly liked, they found the variety of the work enjoyable, and the opportunity to help people was satisfying. They felt that the service users found the service useful, and that it was satisfying when individuals made even a little progress. They also reported that there were many opportunities for learning, general personal development and developing experience.

▶ Areas of concern or aspects of the job they disliked included the feeling that it could sometimes be lonely and isolating, because they were not working closely with other staff on a day-to-day basis. Although acknowledged as a part of the job, service users' changeable motivation and mental state was sometimes seen as frustrating.

▶ A number of service users and their keyworkers were asked what they liked best about the Home Response Service. Service users particularly valued having a friendly relationship with their worker, and being able to get out and about because of the service. Most of the keyworkers highlighted the flexibility of the service and its client focused nature.

▶ After one year, keyworkers were asked to compare the amount of time they each spent with their clients before and after they started receiving the Home Response service. Two thirds reported no difference, while a third spent less time following the uptake of the HRS. Just under half the keyworkers said they used their time more appropriately with these users after they had engaged with the HRS.

▶ Other stakeholders highlighted a primary strength of the service as its "ordinary" low-key nature and the focus it had on building non-professional relationships and engaging service users in everyday activities.

Knowsley Community Support Service and the Social Networks Project

▶ The Community Support Service and the Social Networks Project were jointly evaluated. Ten users of the Community Support Service took part in the evaluation, of whom six were also engaged with the Social Networks Project. However, as the SNP had been established only a few months earlier, most of the findings relate to the CSS.

▶ The CSS appeared to meet its aim of helping users to live independent, ordinary lives in their own community, and all the service users interviewed were satisfied with the help they received. Many felt their social life had improved since using the CSS, due to help with getting out of the house and undertaking tasks such as shopping. Some CSS users had also been introduced to Social Networks Project, which had provided a way of engaging in social activities, such as playing a sport or going out for a drink. They saw the service as different to others they received, being less formal and more like a supportive friendship.

▶ The service users preferred regular practical support, rather than infrequent keyworker input. They saw their support workers as friends, providing companionship and giving them something to look forward to, while health and social services keyworkers were seen as having a more formal role. Seeing the support workers as friends rather than professionals allowed users to form a good relationship with the support worker, and was an effective way of building confidence and learning social skills.

► The Community Support Service appeared to help users lead more independent lives, improving social skills and self-confidence. Existing relationships were supported and sustained. However, the service did not appear to help users form *new* friendships, apart from with the support workers. This may be something that will happen in time, as users' confidence grows, or it may be a sufficient achievement in itself. Setting realistic targets for people whose lives have been impoverished by their mental health problems over many years is an important part of service planning and evaluation.

► Local professionals had positive views of the Community Support Service, and there was evidence of extensive integration and joint working. The service was useful in meeting the need for help with practical tasks, and assistance in developing social skills. Regular visits from support workers were thought to build up a relationship which statutory sector keyworkers did not have sufficient time, or were unable, to do. The working relationship between PSS and the statutory sector was considered to be good, with both hospital-based and community-based teams praising PSS's Knowsley team. These strong links and knowledge of each other's work were given as reasons why PSS was highly regarded and received referrals in preference to an in-house, social services-run support service based in the same building as PSS. In addition, PSS was felt to provide stimulating social support, and the project was regarded as reliable and well-managed.

► In the Social Networks Project, taking part in the group social activities may have the added benefit of users developing friendships which continue outside the group. However, the activities themselves may be enough to improve individuals' quality of life. Some users may find repeated social interactions too stressful, or may lack the opportunities to meet people outside the group. As the Social Networks service is only recently established, these issues could be addressed as it develops further.

Leathermarket Gardens Good Neighbour Scheme

► The evaluation design was significantly revised, because the small number of clients meant that it was not possible to evaluate it in the way originally planned. Instead, more attention was paid to the process of setting up the scheme.

► Ten people were identified through the caseload of the Community Support Team as experiencing long-term severe mental health problems, with varying degrees of social isolation difficulties, and living within the defined catchment area. Five of these became successfully engaged within the befriending scheme.

► The core personnel of Project Manager, Project Supervisor, and Project Administrator successfully established strong working links between the partnership agencies, particularly the statutory organisations.

► Commitment towards the idea of outreach befriending schemes, as an essential way of tackling the issues of stigma and information-sharing, was reflected in a desire to continue informal support for the existing clients beyond the funding period.

► Delays in obtaining funding, following the initial identification of local need, led to a loss of interest among the potential Good Neighbours and statutory sector referrers. Despite the enthusiasm and efforts of the staff, ongoing difficulties with funding, recruitment of volunteers, and attracting referrals, led to the scheme's closure after only two years.

Speke Options

▶ Nine of the ten users interviewed thought that the quality of Speke Options was either excellent or good, 80% thought the service met all or most of their needs, and 90% felt very or mostly satisfied with it.

▶ Forty per cent of the sample said that they visited someone who was not a family member either daily or weekly, while a further 40% said that they had not visited anyone in the last year, illustrating the high level of social isolation experienced by many users.

▶ Measures used to rate users' social functioning showed no significant change over six months. However, the users of Speke Options are a relatively stable group of socially isolated people with severe mental health problems, and their disabilities are social rather than behavioural. The role this service takes in providing social support maintains individuals' level of health, allowing them to cope with life in the community by developing companionship and self confidence in a non-stigmatising way, and reducing isolation.

▶ For the subjective quality of life questions, users reported an improvement at the six month follow up. This subjective quality of life 'feel-good' factor is very important, as although there were no objectively measured improvements in users' quality of life, they felt better and were more positive about their lives. Eight out of the ten service users' overall subjective quality of life score was higher at the six month follow up.

▶ Although all users were registered with a GP, and all except one was also in contact with other services, having most frequent contact with CPNs and social workers, there seemed to be little in the way of inter-agency care plans for any of them, so joint reviews and work with clients on a formal basis is limited.

▶ Key informants identified the service's good points as its user-led aspect and its flexibility. In addition, those who had referred people to the service felt confident that procedures were appropriate and that referrals were followed up and engaged. Informants from both the voluntary and statutory sectors felt they could work well with the project, as long as there were clear aims and boundaries.

▶ The service was valued by professionals, who considered it as an option for people on their caseload. In addition, it demonstrated to other workers the lack of service provision in their areas.

Learning points:

▶ In view of what the services evaluated provide, they cannot be said to be replacing statutory services, rather they are complementary to them, filling gaps which would not otherwise be filled. Few health trusts or social services departments would see it as their role to provide low-level social support, even to people who should clearly be among their highest priority because of their severe and enduring mental health problems. However, the provision of practical, emotional and social support by other agencies may relieve the demand on other services for these types of activity, resulting in a more appropriate use of more highly-paid professionals' time.

▶ When evaluating support services, some objective measures can be used to assess whether users maintain or improve their social and behavioural functioning, and whether their contact with statutory services decreases. However, the subjective quality of life 'feel-good factor' is an important indicator for services aiming to support isolated people with severe long-term mental health problems. Although there may be no objectively measured improvements in users' quality of life, if they feel better and are more positive about their lives, this is clearly a beneficial outcome.

► An understanding of how paid staff and volunteers feel about the various elements of their work can highlight areas in which further training or support is needed. There is likely to be tension between the satisfaction gained by seeing users improve, and possible frustration when they reach and maintain their optimum level of functioning. Working mostly on a one-to-one basis with clients can produce a trade-off between enjoying a high degree of autonomy, and feeling isolated and unsupported.

► It is important that local statutory services understand and respect the work of the support services, if they are to become an integrated part of the overall service provision.

9 Staffing issues

Two of the services evaluated recruited volunteers to provide support to their clients, while the others used a combination of paid salaried and sessional staff. The issues concerning the recruitment, training, support and supervision for both groups are broadly the same.

The support services took different views about whether to recruit staff with previous professional qualifications, such as mental health nursing or social work and, if so, what balance there should be between qualified and unqualified staff. In some cases there may be a positive disadvantage to having professionally-qualified workers, as this could detract from the ethos of providing a service untainted by institutional attitudes. Other services might prefer to recruit staff with previous professional experience and, perhaps, ready-made links and credibility with the local statutory services, who would understand mental health problems and be able to cope with individuals in crisis.

Similarly, if services are recruiting sessional workers, there may be advantages in having a large number of staff, each working a few hours a week with just one client, rather than fewer staff with larger caseloads. Having a wide pool of workers to draw on may make it easier to match them with the clients, and also provides scope for staff to cover for others who are on leave or sick. On the other hand, it may be more efficient to have a smaller number of sessional staff working more hours, each with several clients, in terms of providing support and supervision to fewer individuals. This model could also give the workers an opportunity to gain wider understanding and experience of the service, and provide a path for career development.

Volunteering to work with people who have serious mental illness requires commitment and continuity, as frequent changes of personnel can be very unsettling. Volunteers need to be available at times when the users want their help, which may be during the evenings and at weekends, when potential volunteers may be unavailable or unwilling to work. In view of the general shortage, a balance has to be struck when recruiting volunteers. For example, people who are undertaking professional or educational courses, or work placements, may be very motivated to work with this group, and may already possess relevant skills and experience, but may not be able to commit themselves for very long. Possible sources include students doing NVQ courses in Caring Skills, students on professional social work courses, and psychology students. A comprehensive review of volunteering in mental health (Bagnall *et al.,* 1997) has shown that the stereotype of a volunteer as a middle-aged, middle-class woman to be at least partially accurate, and there can be particular difficulties in recruiting volunteers from an area of high social deprivation.

Projects relying on volunteers are often reported to have a high turnover of staff, and voluntary organisations with small staff teams may have difficulties arranging staff cover for sickness and holidays. Although in general, larger statutory services have a bigger staff pool and administrative support to draw on, the problem is not unique to the voluntary sector.

Recruiting staff and volunteers locally raises the issue of confidentiality. Particularly in a small and close-knit community, users will need to be assured that their confidentiality will be respected by the service. This can be achieved through careful selection, training and supervision of staff and volunteers.

One approach aimed at overcoming some of the reluctance to volunteer to work with adults who have mental health problems could be to focus initially on working with older people, about whom volunteers may have less anxiety, and gradually working towards engaging volunteers with a younger age group.

Bexley Community Support Scheme

► Staff in the BSS had been given opportunities to develop their roles. One sessional support worker had become a salaried worker, the administrator had taken on an additional role as a sessional support worker, and the management of the service was now shared jointly by the two senior members of staff. Additionally, instead of working exclusively in one-to-one sessions with clients, several workers had become involved in group activities with other workers and their clients. BSS had opted to appoint senior staff with obvious abilities, personal qualities and potential, rather than professional qualifications, aiming to help them to develop and increase their skills in the job through training, support and supervision. This also reflected the scheme's wish to provide a socially-orientated service rather than one tied to the medical model, which might have been harder to achieve with staff who had long experience of working in hospital-based services.

Portadown Home Response Service

► The Portadown Home Response Service chose to appoint a co-ordinator on a professional staff grade, with a relevant professional qualification and experience in adult mental health and supervisory management. Their role included recruitment, induction and identifying the training needs of the Home Response Workers, ongoing supervision and support, processing all referrals to the service, liaison with statutory professionals, and monitoring service provision. The Home Response Workers needed some understanding of mental illness, and experience of working directly with this client group. As the workers were going into individuals' homes to work on a one-to-one basis, regular supervision was important. This enabled monitoring of staff to ensure that they were working as intended by the statutory keyworker, supported staff, and ensured that dependencies were not being created, as it was felt this would have negative consequences for the worker as well as the service user.

Speke Options

► The Speke Options Development Worker was the only paid member of staff. The service experienced difficulty in recruiting volunteers, and although links were made with the local volunteer bureau this was not a good source of recruits. A local NVQ course in carer skills, and professional social work and psychology courses, provided students on placement, some of whom went on to become volunteers.

Learning Points:

► Devising and implementing staffing policies can be very time-consuming, but they are essential to maintaining a high standard of care. Proper support and supervision should address issues of service delivery, staff performance and development, and safety issues.

► It is important to match the type of staff recruited, whether professionally qualified or not, to the needs and ethos of the particular service. The number of sessional staff, and the size of their individual caseloads, also needs to be considered.

► There may be some difficulties in recruiting volunteers, especially in areas of high social deprivation. Publicity material, and training and preparation for the role, must be geared to local needs and sensitivities. For example services could produce a range of information leaflets, for diverse audiences, to bridge the information gap

► Any project employing a small number of staff may experience difficulties in providing cover for sickness and holidays, and some voluntary organisations may have a high turnover of staff, leading to a lack of continuity for users, but these problems are not unique to the voluntary sector.

10 Conclusions

▶ All the services evaluated which are still in operation were provided by voluntary organisations, and received some or all their funding from statutory sources. The voluntary sector has a reputation for being more innovative, creative and flexible than statutory services, providing an alternative model of services, which can be more responsive to the needs, and wishes of users. At the moment, voluntary organisations have a greater capacity than the statutory sector to provide flexible services which are available 'out of hours', although statutory services are increasingly being exhorted to extend their availability in this way.

▶ Given the current climate in health and social care, it seems likely that voluntary organisations will continue to expand and develop their role as providers of services for people with mental health problems. However, as they increasingly become funded by statutory sector purchasers, and subject to rigid contract monitoring, the distinction between the sectors may be reduced or lost.

▶ These services are not replacing statutory health and social services, but are complementary to them, filling gaps which would not otherwise be filled. Providing practical, emotional and social support to people with severe and enduring mental health problems may relieve the demand on other services for these types of activity, resulting in a more appropriate use of professional staffs' time.

▶ Some prejudice still exists within statutory services about working with the voluntary sector, and some may assume that using non-professionally trained staff may cause problems, that voluntary sector workers have less training than statutory workers, and that they are less accountable than statutory organisations. However, as voluntary organisations are increasingly being contracted by statutory funders to provide services to clients with serious mental health problems, the perception that they are 'amateurs' should be dispelled.

▶ In order to maximise their chances of success, voluntary organisations should not accept contracts to provide services which are beyond their remit to deliver, or which should properly be provided within the statutory sector.

▶ Voluntary organisations which maintain a distance from workers in statutory services, such as CPNs and social workers, run the risk of isolation. A reluctance by either sector to share necessary client-related information makes it more likely that things will go wrong.

▶ It is hard to compare the true costs of providing services in each sector, but there is a general perception that the voluntary sector is cheaper. When placing contracts, purchasers of these services should ensure they are looking to get good value for money, and not just buying the cheapest option, and they should devise ways of monitoring the contract which include qualitative measures of user satisfaction and the views of other key individuals and organisations, as well as quantitative data. The subjective quality of life 'feel-good factor' for isolated service users with severe and enduring mental health problems should not be overlooked. Although there may be no objectively measured improvements in users' quality of life, if they feel better and are more positive about their lives through using the support scheme, this is an important outcome.

References

Bagnall, S., Warner, L. and Ford, R. (1997) *Is There Anybody Out There? A guide to recruiting volunteers in mental health.* London: The Sainsbury Centre for Mental Health.

Department of Health (1996) *Health Service Guidelines: The spectrum of care – a summary of comprehensive local services for people with severe mental health problems.* LASSL(96)16, HSG(96)6, NHS Executive.

Larsen, D., Atkisson, C., Hargreaves, W. and Nguyen, T. (1979) Assessment of client/patient satisfaction: development of a scale. *Evolution and Programme Planning,* Vol **2**, 197-207. Pergammon Press.

Lehman, A. F. (1983) The well being of chronic mental patients: Assessing their quality of life. *Arch General Psychiatry,* **40**, 369-373.

Netten, A. and Dennett, J. (1996) *Unit Costs of Health and Social Care.* PSSRU, University of Kent at Canterbury.

Rosen, A., Hadzi-Pavlovic, D. and Parker, G. (1989) The Life Skills Profile: a measure assessing function and disability in schizophrenia. *Schizophrenia Bulletin,* **15**, 325-337.